This In

By Liza Charlesworth

ISBN: 978-1-339-02790-6

Art Director: Tannaz Fassihi; Designer: Tanya Chernyak
Photos © Getty Images and Shutterstock.com.

1 2 3 4 5 6 7 8 9 10   68   32 31 30 29 28 27 26 25 24 23
Printed in Jiaxing, China. First printing, August 2023.

This insect has spots.
It landed on a rabbit
in the grass. Flap, flap!

That insect can hop.
It jumped on a stack
of plastic plates.

Can you see the black insect
on top of the napkin?
It is just resting.

Can you see the insect
with fine white wings?
It is by a picnic basket.

This insect is a sneak!
It's bright green and is
hidden on a leaf.

That insect likes to creep.
It crept on a pumpkin
in a patch. Buzz, buzz!

Yikes! This insect is on a kid.
But he is not a bit upset.
He thinks bugs are fantastic!